This SpongeBob SquarePants Annual
belongs to:

....

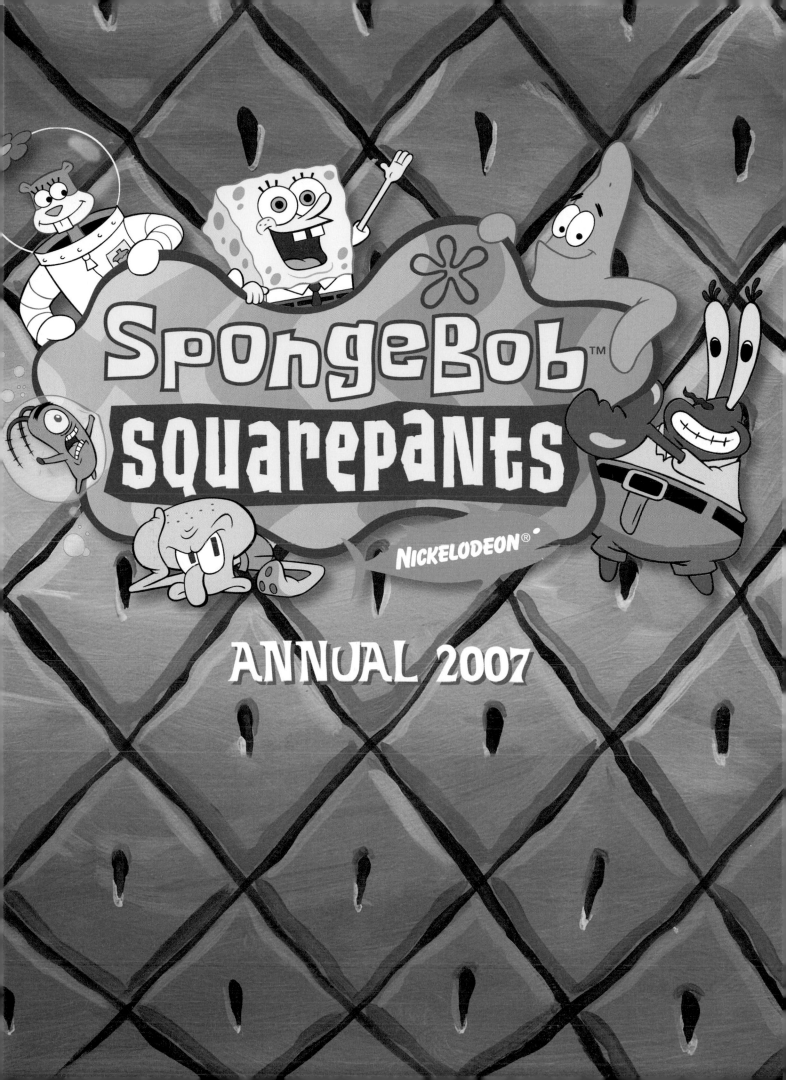

CONTENTS

Edited by Brenda Apsley **Designed by Graham Wise**

EGMONT
We bring stories to life
Published in Great Britain in 2006 by Egmont UK Limited,
239 Kensington High Street, London W8 6SA. All rights reserved. Printed in Italy.
ISBN 978 1 4052 2614 1
ISBN 1 4052 2614 5
1 3 5 7 9 10 8 6 4 2

SPONGEBOB SQUAREPANTS

ALL YOU
- [ ] ever **NEEDED** to know
- [ ] **THOUGHT** there **WAS** to know
- [ ] never ever **WANTED** to know

(Please tick as applicable.)

WHAT? SpongeBob SquarePants is a bright yellow sea sponge. He's a walking, talking ocean-dweller who got his name because:
1. He's a **SPONGE**;
2. He's **SQUARE**, and
3. He wears: **PANTS!**

WHO?

SpongeBob is a cheerful kind of sponge. He always looks on the bright side, no matter what. He means well, but he's disaster-prone, and trouble always seems to be just around the corner, waiting to ambush him. Things can – and do – go wrong. Badly wrong.

WHERE?

SpongeBob lives in Bikini Bottom, an underwater ocean city in the South Pacific. There's lots to do there. You can:
1. Explore the sea grasses and corals that grow in the JellyFish Fields;
2. Fish for stinging jellyfish;
3. Camp in Sea Fan Forest;
4. Surf, play ball or get a sun tan on Mussel Beach.

HOME?

SpongeBob lives in a fully furnished, two-storey pineapple house. You can't miss it, it's next to Patrick's Rock and Squidward's Easter island Head.

WITH?

SpongeBob lives with Gary, a snail who's the ideal pet because he doesn't talk back. He does have his uses though: he can tie shoelaces (don't ask), and though he's a snail-of-no-words he does **meow**, cat-style.

SPONGEBOB LIKES:

1. His job as a fast-food cook at the Krusty Krab. He's famous for his deep-fried Krabby Patties and is always trying to cook the perfect one in the hope that it will earn him the title of Employee of the Month;
2. His best friend and neighbour, a pink starfish called Patrick Star;
3. Thinking about **VERY HARD** Questions;
4. Tighty-whitey underpants;
5. Fishing for wild jellyfish – with a butterfly net. They may sting, but jelly does make the **BEST** sandwich.

DISLIKES:

1. Nothing really – though he **IS** terrified of Bikini Bottom's resident ghost, the Flying Dutchman.

Patrick Star

ALL YOU
- [ ] ever **NEEDED** to know
- [ ] never ever **WANTED** to know
- [ ] **WISHED** you didn't know

(Please tick as applicable.)

WHAT? Patrick Star is a pink starfish who got his name because
1. He's star-shaped, and ...
2. What else would you call a starfish but Patrick?

WHO?

Patrick is a simple kind of guy. He does have a brain, but he doesn't manage to use it too often.

Bikini Bottom
Official identification
(This is Not a Driver's License!)
Patrick Star
120 Conch St. Bikini Bottom
AI359723

PATRICK STAR

WHERE?

Like his very best friend and neighbour SpongeBob, Patrick lives in the under-ocean city of Bikini Bottom.

HOME?

Patrick lives on the underside of his rented house called 'Rock'. He likes it because it's next-door-but-one to SpongeBob's pineapple house.

WITH?

Sadly, Patrick lives with no one.

Patrick Likes:

1. SpongeBob. He's Patrick's all-time hero. Patrick believes every word SpongeBob utters. He does whatever SpongeBob tells him to do. He goes wherever SpongeBob tells him to go. This is NOT wise, and almost always lands him in trouble ...
2. Sleeping on the underside of rocks;
3. Lying dormant on the underside of rocks;
4. Being puzzled: For more on this see pages 18 and 66.

Dislikes:

1. Maybe there was something – but Patrick FORGOT what it was a long time ago.

SQUIDWARD TENTACLES

WHAT? Squidward Tentacles is a grey-green octopus who got his name because:
1. He's not a squid, and
2. He has tentacles (six of them).

WHO? Squidward is a rather high-class, superior type of guy who works with SpongeBob at the Krusty Krab.

WHERE? Squidward is another resident of Bikini Bottom.

Home? Squidward lives between SpongeBob and Patrick in his angry-looking Easter Island Head.

With? Squidward lives all alone, which is just as well – see Likes 1 and 2 and Dislikes 1 to 6 below.

SQUIDWARD LIKES:

1. Playing his clarinet very loudly – and very badly – in the Bikini Bottom Philharmonic Orchestra;
2. Conducting recordings of Beethoven's music. Loud recordings;
3. Having a tentacle-manicure every Thursday.

DISLIKES:

1. His job at the Krusty Krab. He thinks working as a waiter is WAY beneath him. He wouldn't do it if he didn't need the money;
2. His boss, Mr Krabs;
3. The Krusty Krab customers;
4. SpongeBob SquarePants;
5. EVERYONE;
6. EVERYTHING.

Mr Krabs

WHO? Mr Krabs is a crab who got his name because:
1. He's a crab.

WHAT? Mr Krabs is the boss of the Krusty Krab Fast Food restaurant where SpongeBob works. It's in a converted lobster pot.

WHERE? You guessed it – Mr Krabs also lives in Bikini Bottom.

HOME? The money-hungry crustacean does have a home, but he spends almost all his time at the Krusty Krab, so he can earn even more money.

Mr Krabs Likes:
1. Pearl, his daughter;
2. Making MONEY. He just can't get enough of it;
3. Counting his money. Over and over again;
4. SpongeBob – but only because his fry cook will work very long hours for very LITTLE money.

Dislikes:
1. Spending money – unless it's on Pearl.

WITH? Mr Krabs lives with his whale of a daughter, Pearl. He spoils her rotten.

ALL YOU
- [ ] ever WANTED to know
- [ ] ever DREAMED of knowing
- [ ] WISHED you didn't know

(Please tick as applicable.)

13

Sandy Cheeks

What?

Sandy Cheeks is a squirrel. She got her name because:

1. She's the colour of sand, and ...
2. She has cheeks, two of them.

WHO? Sandy can live under the ocean because she wears a special airsuit and helmet so she can breathe. She's a thrill-seeking, all-action kind of girl and SpongeBob has a real crush on her. He'll do **ANYTHING** to spend time with her, even if that involves taking part in dangerous stunts that require him to wear a crash helmet and book a hospital bed in advance.

WHERE? Sandy is Bikini Bottom's only resident rodent. She's from Texas.

HOME? Sandy lives in the Treedome, which is an oak tree under glass. It's a special custom-built pressurised air dome where she can breathe air.

WITH? Sandy lives on her own - but SpongeBob would make room for her in his pineapple house any time.

SANDY LIKES:

1. Karate;
2. Surfing;
3. Doing stunts. **DANGEROUS** stunts.

DISLIKES:

1. Loafing around.

PLANKTON

WHat? Plankton is Bikini Bottom's smallest resident.
He got his name because:
 1. He's a piece of plankton.

WHO? Plankton is so small that he's almost invisible to the naked eye. But that doesn't mean he goes unnoticed. Oh, no – he may be small, but he's incredibly NOISY. And SNEAKY. And MEAN. And RUDE. And ANNOYING. He has a HUGE chip on his tiny shoulder. In short (and he is) he's evil-on-legs.

PLANKTON LIKES:
 1. Scheming and planning;
 2. Being bad.

DISLIKES:
 1. Everyone at the Krusty Krab.

WHere? Plankton is the owner of Bikini Bottom's other Fast-Food joint, Plankton's Chum Bucket. It's a dump. Plankton's aim in life is to steal Mr Krabs' world-famous recipe for Krabby Patties so he can put the Krusty Krab out of business, and get SpongeBob to work for him. It's the only way he's ever going to get any customers.

HOme? Plankton's Chum Bucket.

WitH? Plankton has only his evil plans for company.

ALL YOU
- [ ] HOPED you'd ever know
- [ ] NEEDED to know
- [ ] WISHED you didn't know
  (Please tick as applicable.)

Hi, I'm Patrick. Do you like doing stuff? You do? Hey, that's lucky, because here's some stuff. Stuff to do. Remember to take a **L–O–N–G** nap between each puzzle, 'cause they're really tricky!

Absent Friend

Can you figure out which of my friends' names this is?

P O N G O E B B S
S P O N G B O B

Yes, it's my old buddy Pongo Ebbs. Oh, I remember him well!

Big Draw

Would you like to draw me? Here's how.

1. Draw Rock.

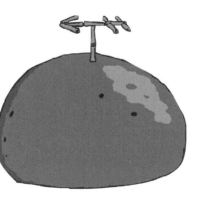

2. Draw me under Rock.

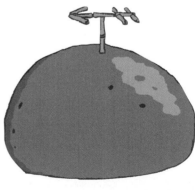

That was easy, wasn't it?

Odd One Out

Which of these Garys is the odd one out?

1.

2.

It's number 3!
He's saying 'meow' really quietly,
and the others aren't.

3.

4.

5.

Join me to form a comedy duo! Can you supply
the punchlines? When it says *Me*, I speak. When
it says *You*, you speak. Got it?

Jokes

Me:	Knock, knock.
You:	_____
Me:	Cock-a-doodle.
You:	_____
Me:	Hey, who let that chicken in here?

Me:	Knock, knock.
You:	_____
Me:	Cook.
You:	_____
Me:	And cuckoo to you!

House-bound

Can you draw a line to show which house I'm going to?

Did you guess? Yes, I'm going to
Squidward's Easter Island Head, next
door to SpongeBob's Pineapple house.

Join the Dots

Join the dots to reveal
the mystery picture.

Hey, it's a
Flagpole!

MIME AFTER MIME

HMM, I WONDER IF THE LATEST ISSUE OF *CLARINET CRAZE* HAS ARRIVED...

EVEN BETTER--*MIME WEEK!* AND HERE I FEARED IT WOULD BE AN UNEVENTFUL DAY.

STOP, MEN! THIS IS IT!

Mime Week

MAGNIFIQUE! THIS LOCATION IS PERFECT FOR MY NEW FILM, 'ENEMY, MIME.' NOW ALL I NEED IS AN ACTOR TO PLAY THE LEAD ROLE.

JEAN-LUC LOBSTAIRE, THE UNRIVALLED *MASTER* OF MIME-THEMED CINEMA!

OH, MR. LOBSTAAAIRRRE...!

SWOOSH

Story and pencils: Mark Crilley. Inks: Jeff Albrecht. Colours: SnoCone Studios. Letters: Comicraft. *SpongeBob SquarePants* created by Steve Hillenburg.

I COULDN'T HELP OVERHEARING... WHILST READING MY LATEST COPY OF *MIME WEEK*, THE MAGAZINE FOR MIME ENTHUSIASTS, WHICH I READ *EVERY* WEEK... THAT YOU ARE IN NEED OF AN ACTOR FOR YOUR NEW FILM.

I CANNOT USE YOU. I NEED SOMEONE YELLOW.

YELLOW? BUT MIMES PAINT THEMSELVES WHITE, NOT YEL--

YELLOW IS THE NEW WHITE. GET WITH THE TIMES!

YOU WANT YELLOW? I CAN DO YELLOW! THERE'S NOBODY AROUND HERE AS YELLOW AS...

HEY, SQUIDWARD, LOOK AT *ME*!

SPONGEBOB! CURSE MY LUCK! IF MR. LOBSTAIRE SEES HIS YELLOW HIDE I'LL LOSE THE PART FOR SURE!

SPONGEBOB, THANK GOODNESS I'VE FOUND YOU! YOU'RE JUST THE MAN TO SAVE BIKINI BOTTOM FROM THIS *TERRIBLE SCOURGE.*

SCOURGE? WHAT SCOURGE?

AND WHAT'S A SCOURGE?

WHY, ALL THIS SEAWEED, OF COURSE. IT NEEDS TO BE REMOVED BEFORE IT DESTROYS ALL THAT WE HOLD DEAR!

REMOVED?

WHY DO YOU THINK THEY CALL IT SEAWEED? THE STUFF'S TOXIC!

GOLLY, I HAD NO IDEA THIS STUFF WAS SO DANGEROUS.

BETTER CLEAR THE WHOLE OCEAN FLOOR WHILE YOU'RE AT IT. WE MUSN'T TAKE ANY CHANCES!

AND SO...

HMM...IF I MIX THE TENTACLE ENRICHING LOTION WITH THIS SQUID INK EMULSIFIER, AND ADD A BIT OF MOISTURIZING FIN CREAM...

TA-DAA... *I'M READY!!*

IT'S SO *OBVIOUS* NOW THAT I THINK OF IT. HOW *ELSE* COULD HE TAKE A BITE OUT OF LIFE?

?!

I DON'T KNOW HOW I WOULD HAVE BEEN ABLE TO CUT THROUGH ALL THIS SEAWEED WITHOUT MY TRUSTY OLD BUCK TEETH.

YOU OKAY, SQUIDWARD? YOU LOOK A LITTLE JAUNDICED.

REALLY, SPONGEBOB, HOW CAN THE GOOD PEOPLE OF BIKINI BOTTOM BE EXPECTED TO GO OUT FOR A STROLL WITH ALL THESE GRAINS OF SAND LYING AROUND? THEY'RE A *HAZARD,* I'M TELLING YOU!

REST EASY, CITIZENS! I WON'T LET YOU DOWN!

GAAAH!

KRASH!

SMASH!

BASH!

HE'S BACK! HE'S BACK TO STEAL MY ROLE!

NOT WHAT I ENVISIONED... BUT NICE, NICE.

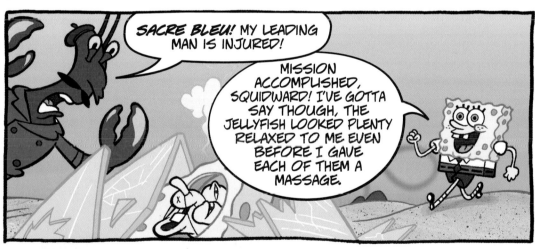

SACRE BLEU! MY LEADING MAN IS INJURED!

MISSION ACCOMPLISHED, SQUIDWARD! I'VE GOTTA SAY THOUGH, THE JELLYFISH LOOKED PLENTY RELAXED TO ME EVEN BEFORE I GAVE EACH OF THEM A MASSAGE.

YOU! YOU'RE PERFECT!

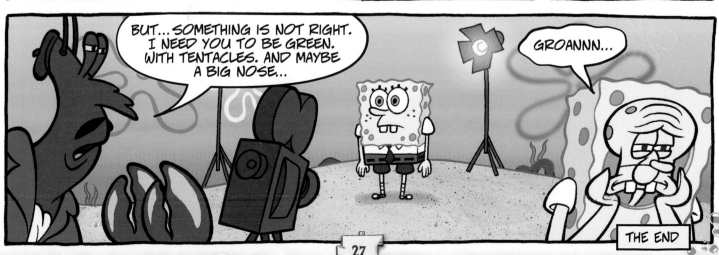

BUT... SOMETHING IS NOT RIGHT. I NEED YOU TO BE GREEN. WITH TENTACLES. AND MAYBE A BIG NOSE...

GROANNN...

THE END

27

Home on De-range

Story, art, and lettering: Sherm Cohen. Colouring: Digital Chameleon. SpongeBob SquarePants created by Steve Hillenburg.

Y'UNDERSTAND NOW?

YEAH. I UNDERSTAND.

SPONGEBOB! HELP! SANDY'S GONNA BREAK HER SEA HORSE IN HALF!!!

Huh?

IT'S TRUE! SHE TOLD ME SHE WAS GONNA **BREAK** HER NEW PET SEA HORSE!

Gasp! LIKE THAT?

HOW COULD SHE WANT TO BREAK A CUTE LITTLE THING LIKE THAT?!

HEY! WAIT FOR ME!

LOOK! SHE'S GOING BACK INSIDE!

HERE'S OUR CHANCE-- PUT ON YOUR GEAR!

LET'S FREE US A SEA HORSE!

HOWDY, PARDNERS!

Yeeee-ha! It's the Bikini Bottom Rangers, Deputy CowBob RanchPants and Deputy Patrick LoneStar Ranger. They're about to show how the Wild West wasn't won! These pictures look the same, but there are 8 things that are different in picture 2. Can you spot them all?

ANSWERS: 1. SpongeBob's hatband has changed colour. 2. one of SpongeBob's teeth has disappeared. 3. SpongeBob's cheek freckles are missing. 4. SpongeBob's jeans have changed colour. 5. one of SpongeBob's spurs is missing. 6. Patrick's foot is missing. 7. Patrick is wearing a different belt buckle. 8. the fringe has disappeared from Patrick's trousers.

The Wild West is just full of cactus plants, and they're pricklier than an angry sea urchin. They come in two sizes: LARGE and LARGER

Are there more large or larger cactuses on this page? Tick the box.

LARGE ✓   LARGER ✗

Deputy CowBob RanchPants and Deputy Patrick LoneStar Ranger need stars to wear if they're to keep the Wild West in order. Can you find two on this page?

ANSWERS: There are 2 more large cactus plants; one star is on the ocean floor, the other star is on a rock.

SpongeBob SquarePants

HEY, PAT! WHAT'CHA DOING?

ADMIRING MY HOUSE.

YES, IT SURE IS ONE FINE ROCK.

AND IT'S STRONG.

HEY!

YOU'RE RIGHT!

UH, OH.

CRACK

RUBBLE RUBBLE

SPONGEBOB, MY HOUSE!

I'M SORRY, PATRICK. I FEEL BAD.

YOU CAN HAVE MY HOUSE!

YUCK! I HATE PINEAPPLE!

Story: Kaz. Pencils: Gregg Shigiel. Inks: Jeff Albrecht. Lettering: Comicraft. Colour: SnoCone Studios. Stonehenge photo by Jeremy Henderson. Mount Rushmore photo by Stefanie Scholler. SpongeBob SquarePants created by Steve Hillenburg.

the end

How to Draw Plankton

Draw Bikini Bottom's most evil resident, Plankton, by following these step-by-step instructions. Make sure you use a pencil with a good eraser because some steps require erasing.

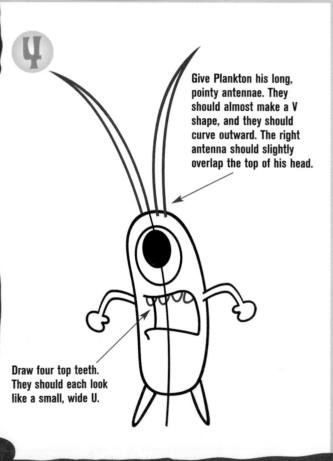

1

Start with a slightly curved vertical line.

Draw a vertical bean shape for Plankton's body.

4

Give Plankton his long, pointy antennae. They should almost make a V shape, and they should curve outward. The right antenna should slightly overlap the top of his head.

Draw four top teeth. They should each look like a small, wide U.

5

Give Plankton an angry brow near the top of his pupil. Add some fuzz with three pointy tips on each end.

Draw his tongue in the bottom right-hand corner of his mouth.

Erase the lines and area shown in blue.

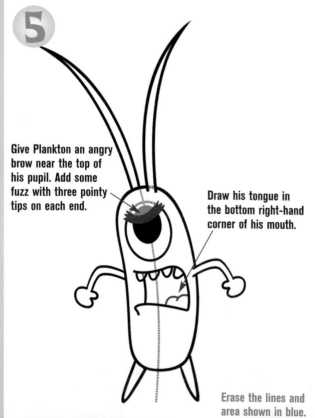

2

Draw an oval for Plankton's eye.

Draw downward-facing tubes for his arms. The right arm should slightly overlap his body.

Give him legs with two carrot shapes.

3

Add a filled-in oval in the upper part of Plankton's eye.

Draw an exaggerated D shape for his mouth.

Add his hands.

Erase the line shown in blue.

6

Add four thin rectangles to each antenna.

Add slight detail to each hand.

Add a wrinkle below Plankton's mouth.

Erase the area shown in blue.

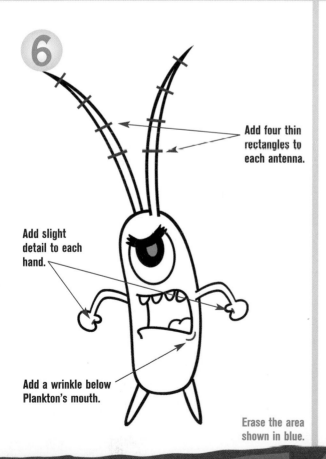

DRAW PLANKTON HERE!

A Plague of Planktons

I can't deny it any longer, I am small!

Yes, Plankton may be small – microscopic, even – but he's evil-on-legs: devious, sneaky and dangerous.

SpongeBob panicked when he heard that Plankton was having himself cloned to make MULTIPLE Planktons. How would SpongeBob spot the REAL Plankton among the almost perfect, hair-raising clones?

This is where you come in. Can YOU identify the real Plankton? Earn a bonus buy-one-get-one-Free Krabby Patty voucher if you can count the number of FAKE Planktons using only the Fingers of one hand!

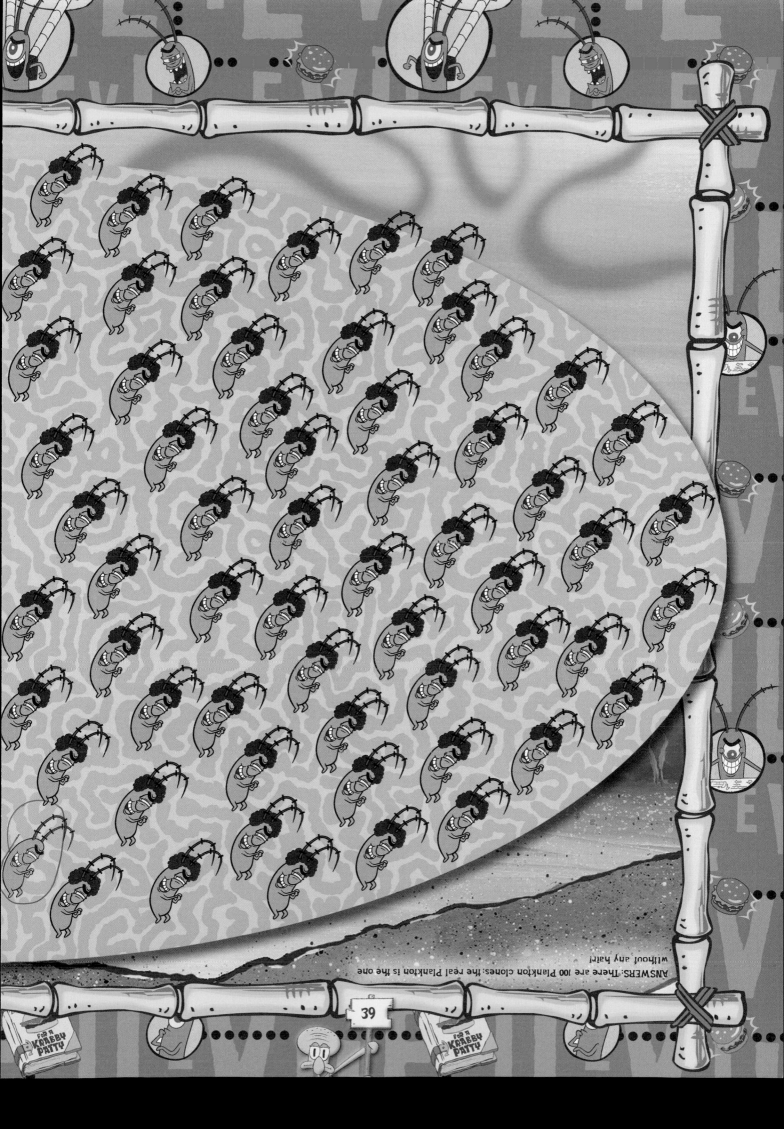

ANSWERS: There are 100 Plankton clones; the real Plankton is the one without any hair!

39

43

Sandy Cheeks

SLURP!

Story: Sam Henderson. Pencils and inks: Vince Deporter. Colouring: Stu Chaifetz. Editor: Dave Roman. SpongeBob SquarePants created by Steve Hillenburg.

WRITTEN + DRAWN BY SAM HENDERSON - 2003

Story: David Lewman. Pencils: Gregg Schigiel. Inks: Jeff Albrecht. Colour: SnoCone Studios. Letters: Comicraft. *SpongeBob SquarePants* created by Steve Hillenburg.

OF COURSE, TO PUT ON A GREAT PUPPET SHOW YOU HAVE TO WRITE A GREAT SCRIPT!

SCRIPT? I THOUGHT IT WAS... UM... NEVER MIND.

CRASH!

HAMMER

AND FINALLY, THE THEATER!

BASH!

SAW!

LET'S SEE... DO I KICK WITH MY LEFT OR MY *OTHER* LEFT?

BANG! BUZZ! ANNOY!

WHAT IN THE UNDERSEA WORLD?!

NOW ALL WE NEED IS AN AUDIENCE.

DON'T BE NERVOUS, LIL' STUPID HEAD.

PUPPET THEATER

LOOK, SON. A PUPPET SHOW!

OH, BOY!

PUPPET THEATER

FREE PUPPET SHOW!

I'M OPTIMISTIC! I'M OPTIMISTIC! I SURE AM OPTIMISTIC!

I'M STUPID! I'M STUPID! SO STUPID!

THEY'RE GIVING PUPPETRY A BAD NAME.

THAT WAS LAME.

PUPPET THEATER

FREE PUPPET SHOW!

WAAAAAAAA!

WAAAAAAA

GEE, THEY DIDN'T LIKE IT.

MAYBE OUR SHOW NEEDS MORE ACTION.

PUPPET THEATER

FREE PUPPET SHOW

LIKE WHAT?

I TOLD YOU TO BE QUIET! STOP ALL THIS NOISE! NOW!

HEY, I JUST GOT AN IDEA FOR A NEW PUPPET!

SOON...

I THINK A CERTAIN *SOMEONE* IS GOING TO BE VERY EXCITED WHEN HE LEARNS HE WAS THE INSPIRATION FOR A NEW PUPPET! WHAT AN *HONOUR!*

I'M OPTIMISTIC AND I'M PROUD!

I AM STUPID AND I'M LOUD!

I HEARD THIS SHOW WAS LAME.

I THINK YOU HEARD RIGHT.

HI, THERE, BIG NOSE!

BONK

BE QUIET! STOP ALL THIS NOISE! NOW!

HEH, HEH!

NOW *THAT'S* COMEDY!

ONE PUPPET SHOW LATER...

THANK YOU! THANK YOU!

WE LOVE YOU, BIG NOSE!

YAY!

BRAVO!

AND IN ARTS NEWS, A PUPPET SHOW HAS TAKEN BIKINI BOTTOM BY STORM, THANKS TO ITS STAR, BIG NOSE!

LA LA LA!

DUMB DUMB DUMB!

WE WANT BIG NOSE! WE WANT BIG NOSE!

BONK

BE QUIET!

YAY! BIG NOSE!

MEANWHILE, ACROSS TOWN...

ALL RIGHT, SQUIDWARD. THIS IS IT. GO OUT THERE AND DANCE LIKE YOU'VE NEVER DANCED BEFORE!

HEY! IT'S HIM!

THEY LIKE ME! THEY REALLY LIKE ME!

YAY!

BRAVO!

HEY, BIG NOSE! WHERE'S YOUR CLARINET?

THEY WANT TO HEAR ME PLAY! GOOD THING I NEVER GO ANYWHERE WITHOUT CLAIRY!

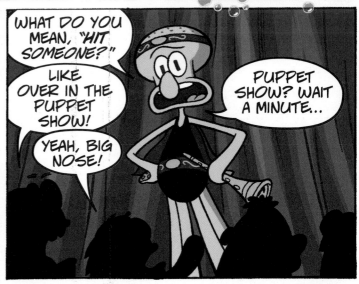

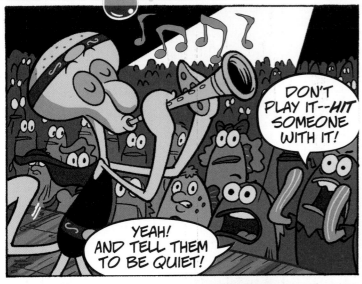

THE END

They were having a high old time – until SpongeBob swam out to catch
a wave on his surfboard and Patrick swam out to join him.

Soon they were heading back for the shore – fast!
"**EXIT PAGE LEFT**!" said SpongeBob.
"Page what?" said Patrick.

Who – or what? – was pursuing SpongeBob and Patrick?
Think up the ugliest, meanest, plain scariest sea monster you can,
draw and colour it in, then write its name – and yours – on the lines.

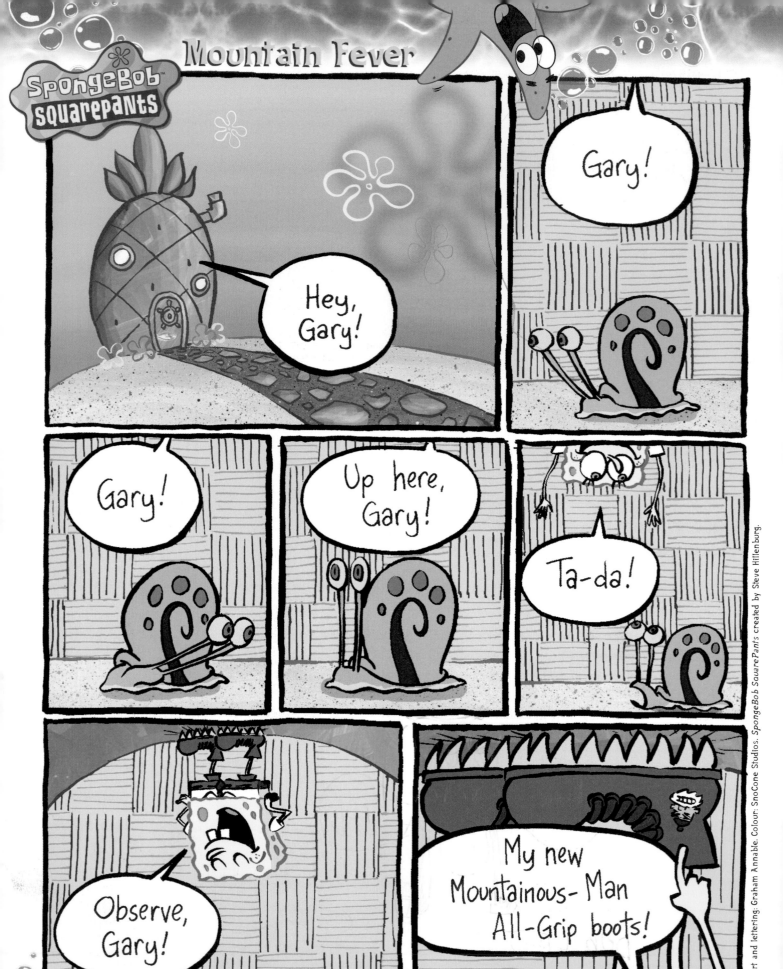

The ultimate in climbing control!

WHAM!

With boots like these there's only one place to go, Gary!

Fish Hook Peak!

Berry's Bend

Fish Hook Peak

You sit tight, little pal!

Pat! Pat!

I'm off to put a flag in Fish Hook!

meow.

Forward march, Patrick!

Marching for-ward, Sponge Bob!

♪ Yodel-lay-hee-hee! ♪

Much later...

Yodel...

hee...hee...

...phew!

We're finally at the foot of the mountain, Patrick!

the end

More Puzzled with Patrick

Here's some more stuff for you to do. It's tricky, so take a tip from me and don't overdo things. Take your time; if you're like me doing one puzzle a week will be just about right!

A Jigsaw Puzzle

Which of these pieces will fit into the jigsaw puzzle to complete the picture?

You can draw in the missing bits if you like.

1

3

5

2

4

6

Seasons

SpongeBob: Patrick, which season does this picture show? You have THREE guesses!

Patrick: Spring?

Patrick: Autumn?

Patrick: Summer?

What's Next?

What comes next?

1 **2** 3

Buckle my shoe?

That's not fair! I need another three guesses!

Hide and Seek

Can you find SpongeBob?

No.

Location, Location, Location

Who's home?

You're right, there's no one home!

Adding Up

What do you get if you add the following …

SpongeBob's top teeth	4
Squidward's tentacles	+ 4
the flowers on Sandy's air dome	+ 4
the number of Plankton's eyes	+ 4
the stings on a pink jellyfish?	+ 4
	= ___

I know what I get! A **VERY** bad headache.

Short Shorts

Which is the odd picture out?

1.

2.

3.

It's number 1. The other shorts aren't my size.

SpongeBob's Square Quiz

1 Squidward Tentacles is:
- a) a squid,
- b) a tentacle, or
- ✓ c) an octopus?

2 The Chum Bucket is owned by:
- ✓ a) Plankton,
- b) Mr Krabs, or
- c) Sandy Cheeks?

3 What makes the best sandwich in the ocean? Is it:
- a) tuna,
- b) seaweed, or
- ✓ c) jelly?

4 Sandy Cheeks comes from Arizona:

True ☒   or   False ☑

5 I live in a fully furnished, undersea fruit house. Is it:
- a) a bunch of grapes,
- b) a melon, or
- c) a pineapple?

6

This is the Bikini Bottom ghost.
What is his name? Is it:
   a) the Flying JellyFish,
 ✓ b) the Flying Dutchman, or
   c) the Frying Cook?

7

Squidward Tentacles lives in
Easter Island Head.

True   or   **False**

X   ✓

8

Which of my neighbours
has a daughter called
Pearl? is it:
   a) Mr Krabs,
   b) Patrick Star, or
   c) Plankton?

9

What colour is my tie? Is it:
   a) pink with yellow spots,
 ✓ b) red, or
   c) black?

10

Who lives here? Sandy
What is the name of the house? The Dome